l'Aventure de Sebastian

Morgan Landis
Illustré par Jacqueline Bell

Creo En Ti

Il était une fois un cochon marchant près de l'étang. Il regardait son reflet et il était triste.

Once upon a time a pig was walking near a pond. He was looking at his reflection and he was sad.

Il a dit: «J'aimerais avoir l'air différent. Je ne ressemble pas aux autres animaux."

He said, "I wish I looked different. I do not look like the other animals."

Il pensait qu'il serait enfin heureux s'il se changeait pour ressembler à d'autres animaux.

He thought that he would finally be happy if he changed himself to look like other animals.

Sébastien a vu une paresse suspendue à un arbre. Il avait un nez parfait. C'était si petit et magnifique.

Sebastien saw a sloth hanging from a tree. He had a perfect nose. It was so tiny and looked beautiful.

«Je veux un nez comme ça», pensa Sebastian. Alors le cochon a mis de la terre sur son nez pour cacher son gros nez volumineux.

"I want a nose like that," thought Sebastian. So the pig put some dirt on his nose to hide his big bulky nose.

Sébastien aimait son nez magnifique!

Sebastian loved his beautiful nose!

Sébastien a rencontré un cheval qui avait de belles, longues jambes. Le cheval courait dans un champ et il avait l'air de s'amuser.

Sébastien voulait avoir de longues jambes comme le cheval, il a donc construit des échasses avec des branches.

Sebastien saw a horse who had beautiful, long legs. The horse was running in a field and looked like he was having fun.

Sebastien wanted to have long legs like the horse; so, he built stilts with branches.

C'était difficile de marcher avec les échasses mais Sébastien les aimait.

It was hard to walk with the stilts but Sebastien loved them.

Sébastien a rencontré un suricate. Le suricate était allongé sur la branche d'un arbre. Il avait de belles petites oreilles et Sébastien pensa: "J'aimerais avoir de telles oreilles." Il a donc attaché ses oreilles pour les faire ressembler a celles du suricate.

Next, Sebastien saw a meerkat. The meerkat was lounging on the branch of a tree. He had beautiful small ears, and Sébastien thought, "I wish I had ears like that." So, he tied his ears to make them look like the meerkat.

Sébastien ne pouvait pas bien entendre avec ses oreilles attachées, mais elles avaient l'air si mignonnes et il était heureux.

Sebastien could not hear well with his ears tied up, but they looked beautiful and he was happy.

Alors que Sébastien marchait, il trouva un lémurien. “Regarde sa belle queue!” il s’est exclamé. Je aimerais une queue comme ça."

As Sebastien was walking he saw a lemur. “Look at his beautiful tail!" he exclaimed. "I want a tail like that.”

Il a donc attaché des herbes longues à sa petite queue frisée.

So, Sebastien tied long grass to his curly, little tail.

Sebastian retournait à son étang pour regarder son nouveau reflet. Soudain, un panda a sauté dans l'étang et a éclaboussé Sebastian!

Sebastian was returning to his pond to look at his new reflection. Suddenly, a panda jumped into the pond and splashed Sebastian!

Sébastien était en colère et cria "Pourquoi m'as-tu éclaboussé? Tu as ruiné tout mon dur travail!"

Le panda a répondu: «Je suis vraiment désolé. Pourquoi portiez-vous toutes ces choses? "

Sebastien was angry and shouted "Why did you splash me? You ruined all my hard work!"

The panda replied, "I am so sorry. Why were you wearing all these things?"

Sébastien regarda toute la boue, les échasses et les longues herbes qu'il avait mises. "Je pensais que tout m'aiderait à m'aimer moi-même. Je voulais être plus heureux et avoir confiance en moi."

Sebastien looked at the mud, the stilts, and the long grass he had on. "I thought everything would help me to love myself. I wanted to be happier and to have confidence in myself."

Le panda a dit: "Tu es parfait comme ça et tu n'as pas besoin de toutes ces choses pour te rendre heureux. La solution est simple, tu dois t'aimer toi-même."

The panda said, "You are perfect just the way you are and you do not need all these things to make you happy. The solution is simple, you must love yourself."

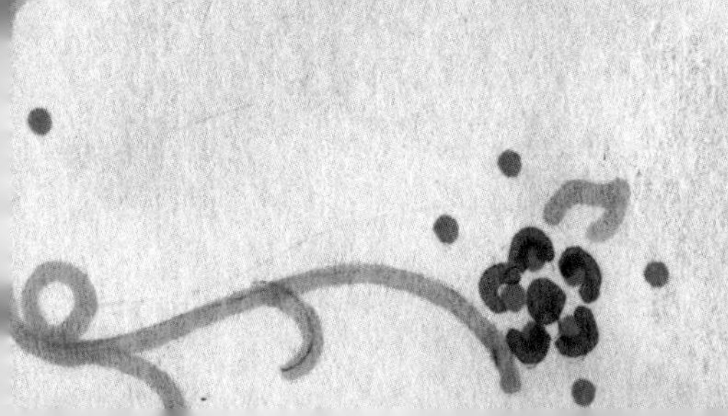

Sebastian réalisa qu'il n'avait pas besoin de se changer pour être parfait. Il était heureux.

Sebastian realized that he did not need to change himself to be perfect. He was happy.

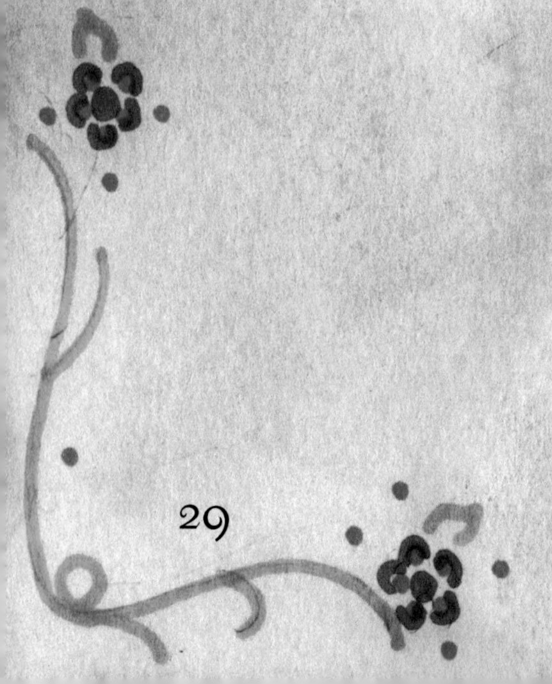

About the Author

Morgan Landis is a graduate of Northern High School in Dillsburg, Pennsylvania. She plans to become a Speech Therapist and will study at Lebanon Valley College. Morgan enjoys hiking, kayaking, field hockey, track and field, and spending time with her friends, family and her dog, Daisy! She hopes this book will encourage young children to love themselves for who they are. L' Adventure de Sebastian is Morgan's first book.

About the Illustrator

Jacqueline Bell is a graduate of Northern High School in Dillsburg, Pennsylvania. She is attending Penn State University in the Fall of 2019 and is planning on majoring in K-12 Art Education with a minor in psychology. At the age of 18, Jacqueline enjoys spending time with her golden retriever and painting. Jacqueline's biggest inspiration is her mom who also shares a passion for art as well as her favorite teacher Jennifer Brink (AP Art). She hopes to one day inspire children to express themselves through Art and love themselves for who they are. This is the first book that Jacqueline has illustrated.

Our Creative Director

Lisa Pietropola is the Creative Director of Creo En Ti Media and has spent 15 years in both the public and private school systems advocating for world languages. Lisa has built her career on establishing confidence in her students and using that confidence to empower lives. The recipient of the Outstanding Teacher of the Year Award, 2017, Lisa holds a Master of Arts degree in Spanish from Saint Louis University, Madrid, Spain. Lisa's years living abroad molded her approach to language learning. She continues to teach and inspire students today and is certified in both Spanish and English as a Second Language. Along with leading educational trips abroad, Lisa enjoys traveling with her husband and their two daughters.

"I am most proud of this endeavor not only because of the empowerment of second language learning, but also because we are raising a generation of students who have educators who believe in them."
–Lisa Pietropola

About Creo En Ti Media

Creo En Ti is a Spanish phrase which means "I believe in you." Dante el Elefante began in Lisa Pietropola's AP Spanish class at Northern High School in South Central Pennsylvania as a student-centered, bilingual literacy project designed to promote early childhood literacy. It developed into a cross-curricular endeavor combining art and foreign language content areas. This project created an opportunity for outstanding student work to be published and available to children and educators. Creo En Ti Media strives to give parents and educators the tools to spark an interest in language learning at a young age.

For more information about this project, including lesson plans for Spanish language classes, ESL classes and activities for parents and early childhood educators, please visit our website at www.creoentimedia.com

"Creo en ti means so much more than simply 'I believe in you.' It is the pillar of my teaching philosophy. Educators, like parents, pour their hearts and souls into the growth and success of their children. Students need to be filled with a sense of security before learning can take place. That is where Creo en ti comes in."
–Lisa Pietropola

Creo En Ti

www.creoentimedia.com

Creo En Ti Media
Owl Publishing, LLC.
150 Parkview Heights Road
Ephrata, Pa 17522
717-925-7511
www.OwlPublishingHouse.com

ISBN-13: 978-1-949929-16-4
Library of Congress Control Number- In production

Made in the USA
Columbia, SC
23 September 2020